THE BEAUTIFUL PATTERNS *Colouring Book*

Seek
Buck
Yell
Rook
Maze
U28G
Term

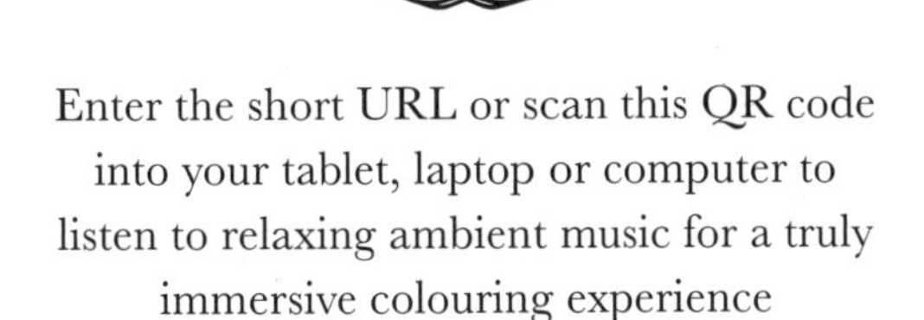

Enter the short URL or scan this QR code into your tablet, laptop or computer to listen to relaxing ambient music for a truly immersive colouring experience

https://youtu.be/vB4CEZZ_loI

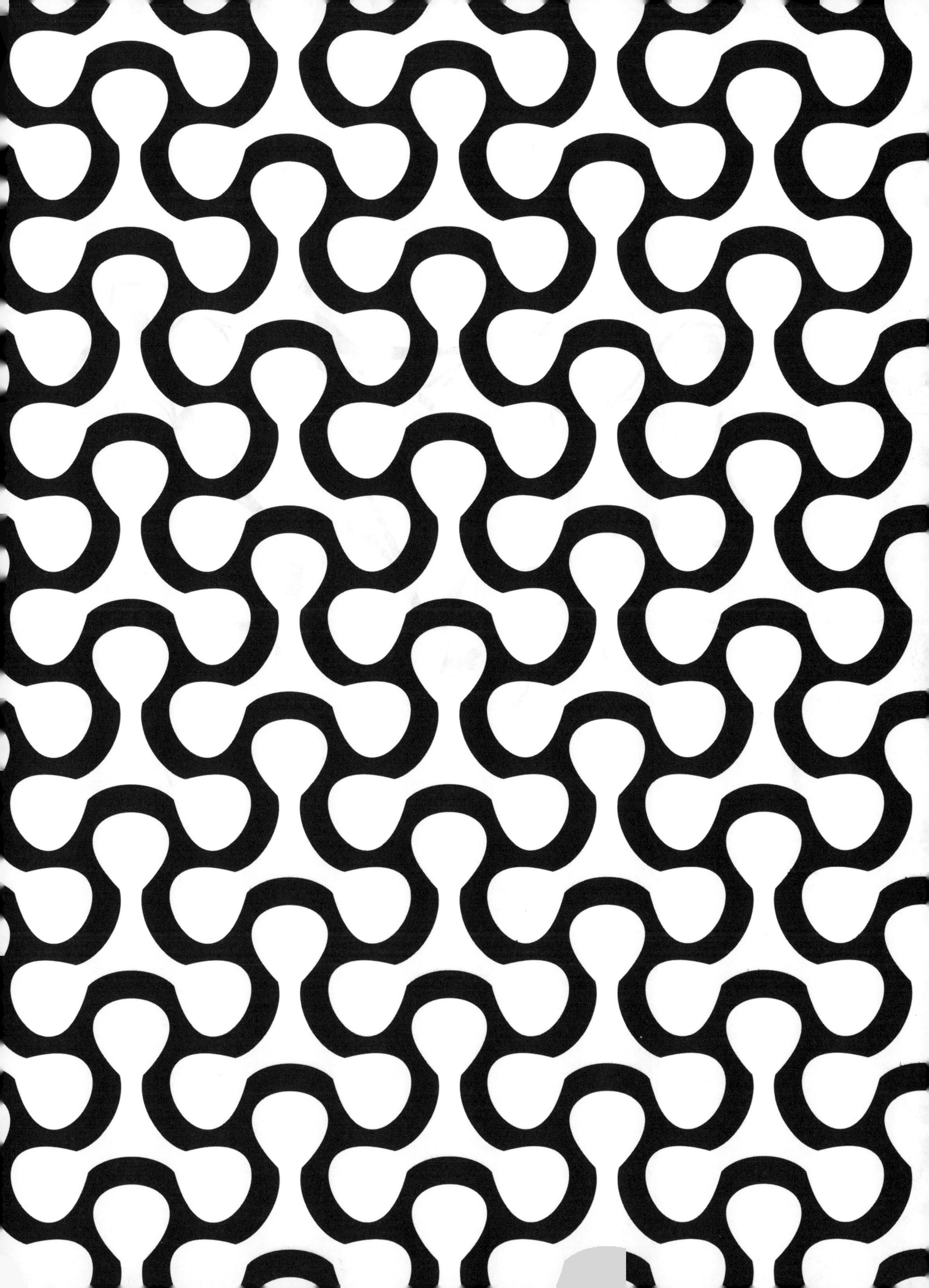

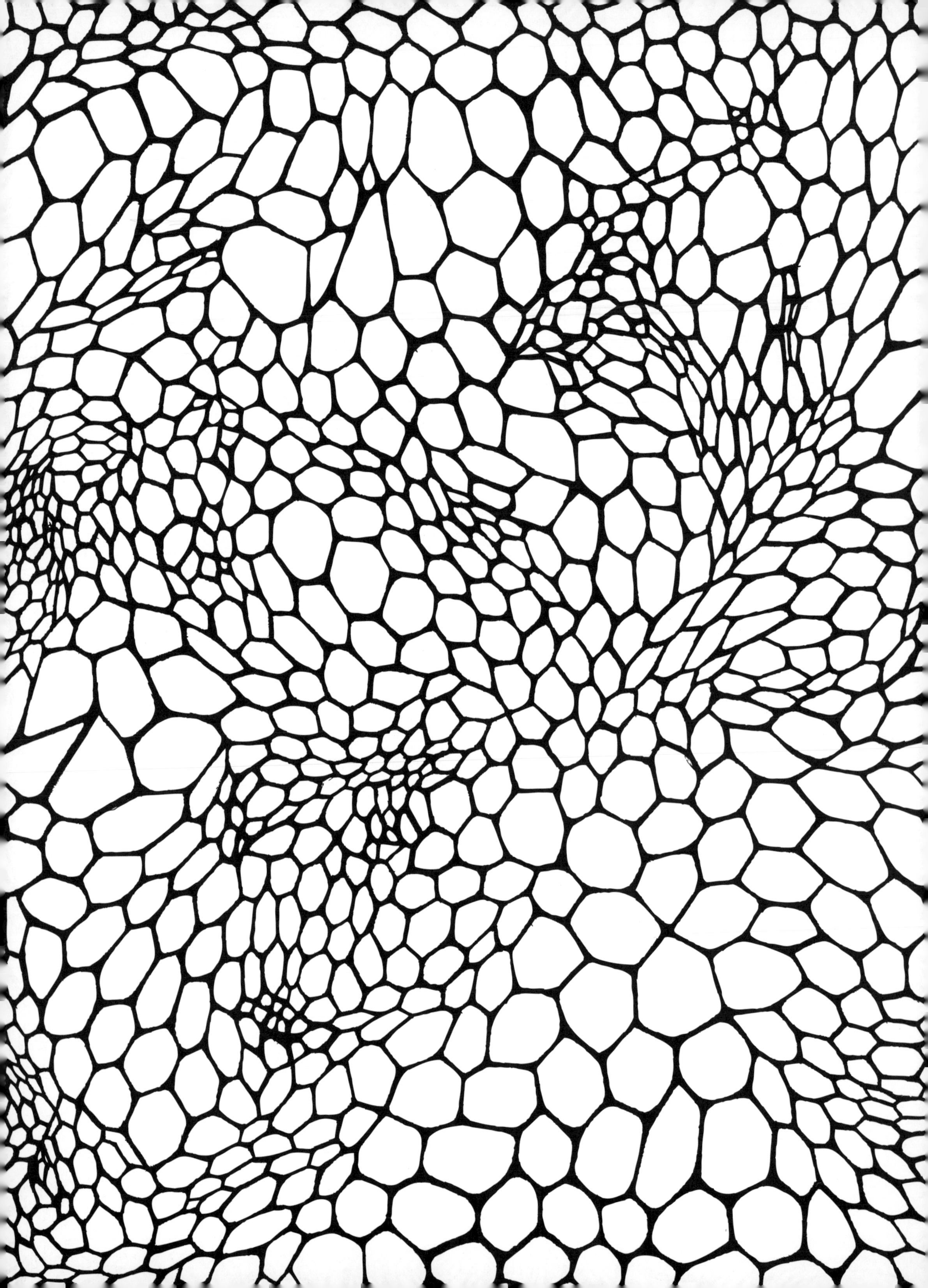

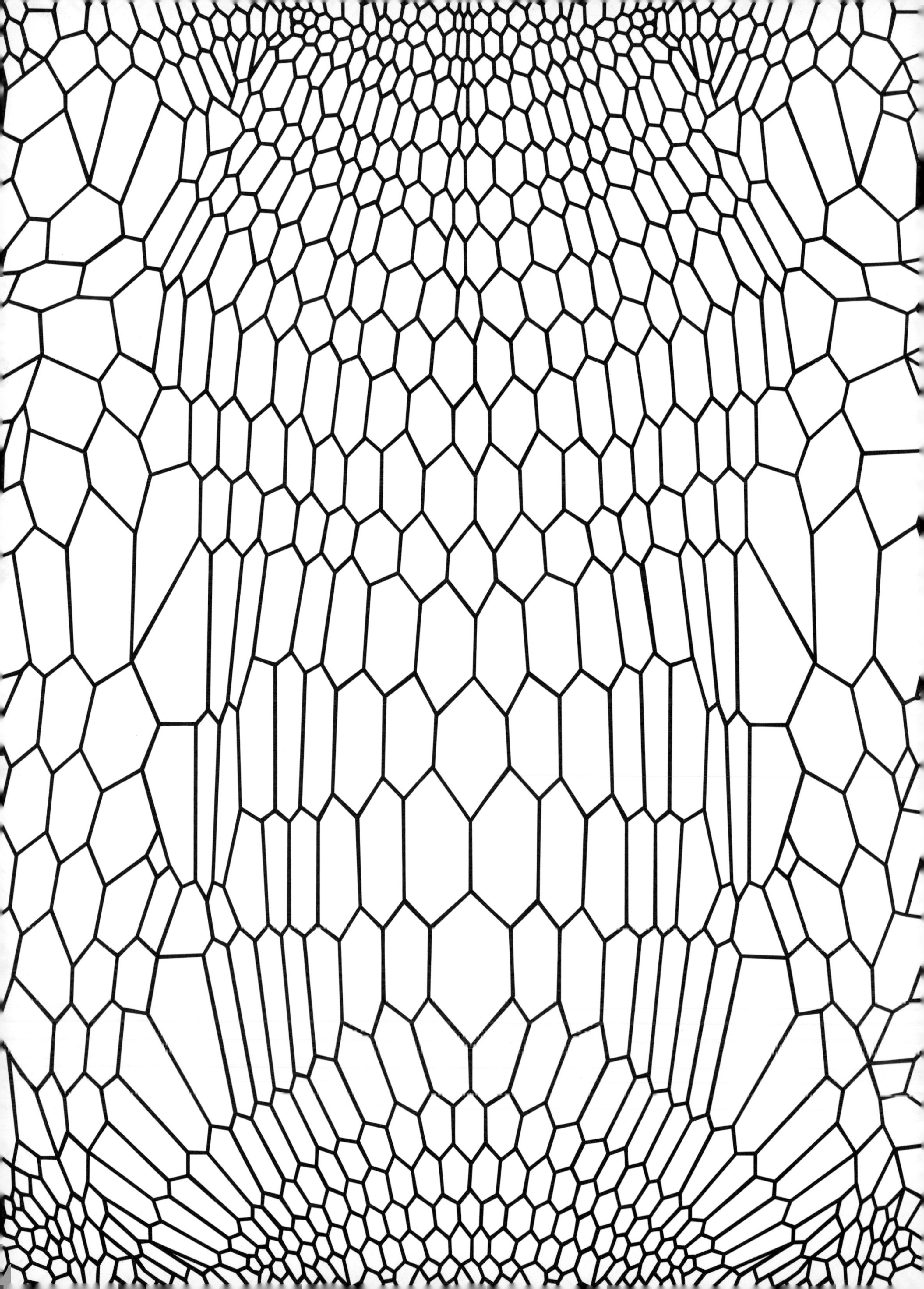

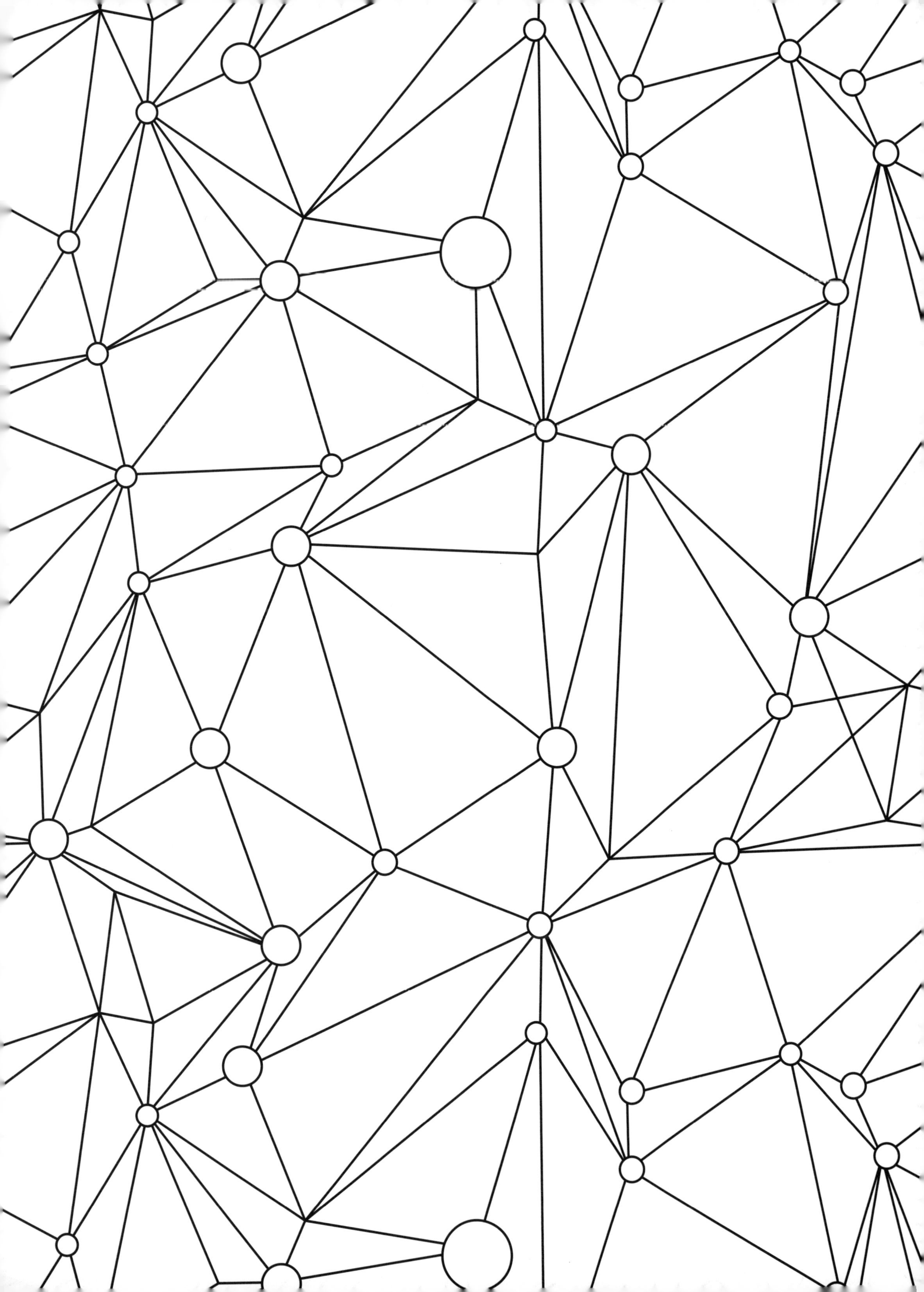

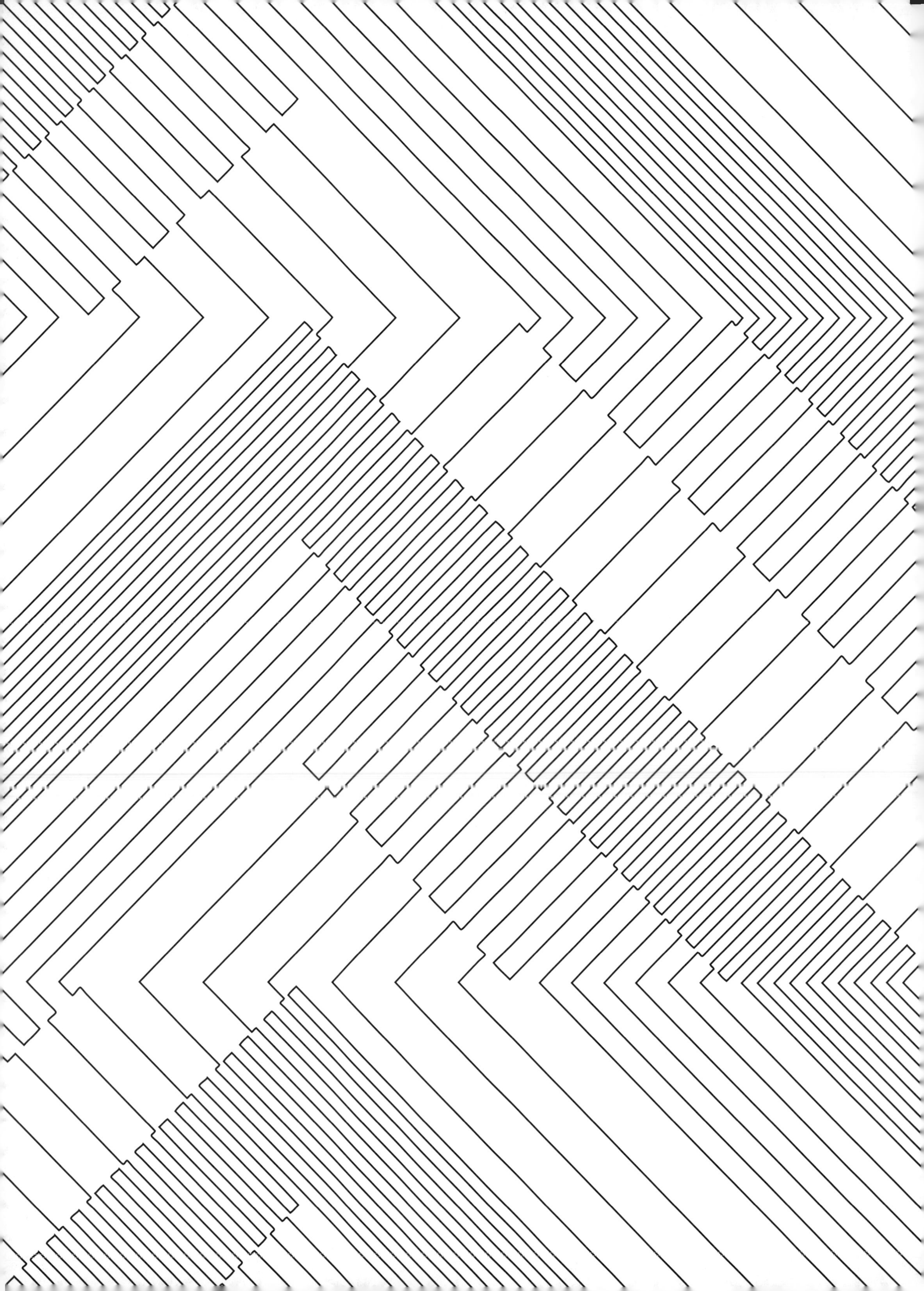

THIS IS A CARLTON BOOK

Published by Carlton Books Ltd
20 Mortimer Street
London W1T 3JW

A CIP catalogue record for this book is available from the British Library

10 9 8 7 6 5 4 3 2 1

ISBN 978-1-78097-863-5

Printed in China

Picture credits: Shutterstock